Queen Maeve's Raging Return to Galway

Patricia Forde
Illustrated by **Derry Dillon**

Published 2014
Poolbeg Press Ltd

123 Grange Hill, Baldoyle
Dublin 13, Ireland

Text © Poolbeg Press Ltd 2014

A catalogue record for this book is available from the British Library.

ISBN 978 1 78199 976 9

Cover design and illustrations by Derry Dillon
Printed by GPS Colour Graphics Ltd, Alexander Road, Belfast BT6 9HP

Queen Maebh's Raging Return to Galway

This book belongs to

MAC – Mythical Activity Control

Mission Info

There was a time, long ago, when Ireland was a place of magic. Now, all the magical people and creatures live in the Otherworld. To people like you, they are just myths and legends. But sometimes they can escape into your world.

Mythical Activity Control guards the doorways to your world. And when someone gets through, it's MAC's job to bring them back.

From the Agent Files:

ÁINE *(pronounced 'AWN-yeh')*
Ancestor:
Áine, Goddess of
Summer and Light.
Personality:
Smart but stubborn.
Loves nature.
Can judge the moods of
people and animals.
Power:
Can talk to animals.
Can travel through
mirrors and polished metal.

FIONN *(pronounced 'Fy-UNN')*
Ancestor:
Legendary warrior Fionn McCool.
Personality:
Clever, sensible, but curious too
and that can get him into trouble.
Power:
Can connect to information from
either world by biting his thumb,
like his ancestor after he tasted
the Salmon of Knowledge.
Can travel through mirrors and polished metal.

TOGETHER, they help keep you safe from the
wild magic of the Otherworld.

Also in the MAC series

Viking Thunder in Dublin
The Banshee Queen of Cork
The Lord in the Lake in Limerick

ALSO...

There are ten Claddagh rings hidden in this adventure. Can you find them?

The tourists loved the swans at the Claddagh, where the River Corrib meets the sea just outside the old walls of Galway city. People said that the swans were the souls of dead fishermen, but the tourists didn't know that. They just knew that the white birds liked bread and looked great in photographs.

"Here, birdie!" one of the Americans shouted. "Check this out!" and he threw them a whole croissant.

The swans looked up eagerly, and the biggest one was just about to snatch the tasty treat when there was a deafening roar.

In an instant the sun disappeared and dark clouds sailed in from the open sea. The temperature dropped from a sunny twenty-five degrees to something that made the tourists shiver and wish they had bought a traditional Aran sweater.

The still water in the Claddagh basin shuddered and an eerie green light descended. The water rose up, as though a giant hand were underneath it, pushing the wave ten metres into the air. Then on the crest of this enormous surge, something appeared: a golden chariot, sparks flying from it in all directions, being drawn by two white horses. In the chariot stood a woman with flowing red hair, a sword in one hand and a shield in the other. On her shoulder sat a small brown-and-white animal – a stoat – with a golden collar around its neck.

"Run!" shouted the American man. "Run for your lives!" And he took off towards Salthill beach.

"Come back!" the figure in the chariot bellowed. "I am a queen!"

Johnny McBride, a local fisherman, looked across at the scene unfolding.

"And not just any queen," he muttered darkly. "If I'm not mistaken that's Queen Maebh herself!"

Up the road at the Fire Station, a fireman was in the bathroom, checking that his hair still looked as perfect as it had earlier that day. He put on a bit of gel and stood back to admire himself. As he did, there was a flash of light that sent him diving to the floor, and out of the mirror leapt two children.

Their names were Áine and Fionn and they were secret agents from the Otherworld. They worked for MAC – Magical Activity Control, and they had the power to travel through mirrors or polished metal. MAC controlled the mirror roads, and Áine and Fionn only had to think of a destination and the roads could find the mirror that was nearest to it.

It was the agents' job to make sure no one from the Otherworld caused trouble in this world.

"Sorry!" Áine said, stepping over the fireman. "Can't stop! On a job."

Out on the street, the agents took off towards the Claddagh.

"I'll have a word with the swans," Áine said. She could talk to animals and birds. Fionn followed her across to the water.

"Calm down!" Áine was saying to the swans. "Yeah . . . yeah . . . A chariot? Okay. She was a queen? Any idea what she wants, this queen? Something about a bull? Are you sure? No! I don't have any bread. Look at the sign! People aren't supposed to feed you. Across the bridge? Okay. Thanks, guys."

"Well?" Fionn said. "What's the story?"

"According to the swans she's come here looking for a bull! They sent her to the museum!"

The two agents took off across the bridge and came to an old stone arch.

Fionn bit his thumb, which was how he connected to information from the myth-web in the Otherworld and the world wide web in ours.

"That's the Spanish Arch," he said as they ran through it. "And that's the museum behind it."

A blonde woman staggered out of the museum towards them. The badge on her jacket said 'Museum Curator'.

"Mad!" she muttered as she passed them. "Maebh! A queen from prehistoric times. How could it be? Mind you, the chariot looked like the real thing . . . she parked it right under the Arch!"

Fionn bit his thumb again. "Maebh, Queen of Connacht," he reported. "Best known for leading the Cattle Raid of Cooley to steal Ulster's prize bull!"

Áine ran after the curator and took her gently by the arm.

"Is she still in the museum?" she asked.

"No!" she said. "She saw a poster for *King Lear* and headed off at speed to Druid Lane."

Fionn stuck his thumb back in his mouth and then reported: "Druid is a famous Galway theatre company, based in Druid Lane."

"Let's go," Áine said. She turned to the blonde woman. "Do you have a mirror in the museum?"

"In the toilets," the woman muttered, looking puzzled. "But . . . why . . ."

The children didn't wait to hear any more.

In Druid Lane, the actors were outside the theatre having a cup of tea. They had been dress-rehearsing *King Lear* and were glad of the break.

They heard the horses before they saw them. Even so, nothing could have prepared them for a golden chariot carrying a very aggressive-looking queen.

"Well!" the Queen called from the chariot. "Where have you hidden your bulls?"

"Bulls?" the man playing King Lear managed to say. "I can assure you, loveen, there are no bulls here."

The actors laughed. Big mistake.

The stoat on the queen's shoulder snarled, baring its short, sharp teeth. The queen pulled her sword. With one swift movement she caught Lear by the tunic with it, and lifted him off his feet.

"You are the King of Connacht, are you not?"

Lear opened and closed his mouth but no words came out.

"The market!" the girl playing Cordelia shouted. "Try the market! For the bull!"

"Thank you!" the Queen said as she dropped Lear, swung the chariot about and took off.

Meanwhile, Áine and Fionn jumped out through the mirror in the Druid dressing room.

As they rushed through the door, Áine almost collided with a very haughty-looking cat.

"Oh sorry," Áine said, "but we're looking for a queen. You can't miss her really – she's got a chariot and two white horses and –"

"Really, darling! Your diction! One must speak clearly if one wishes to be understood. We theatre folk have very keen ears but –"

"Please," Áine interrupted, "have you seen her?"

The cat sighed. "She has gone to the market in search of a bull but . . ."

Áine didn't wait to hear any more. She grabbed Fionn and pulled him back towards the dressing room.

"The market!" she managed to say, before jumping through the mirror, Fionn close behind her.

The market had been devastated – stalls knocked over, chickens running wild, apples rolling down the street. The rector of the Church of Saint Nicholas was standing at the gate with a group of choirboys and girls, looking at the scene in horror.

"We're too late," said Fionn. "No sign of her." He stopped suddenly and looked at the ground. Bending down, he picked up a ring. "It looks old," he said. "Do you think . . . ?"

At that moment a passing chicken stopped and put her head to one side.

"Yer wan, the Queen, dropped it. Not that it's any of my business. I'm not the sort of chicken for gossipin'. Not like some. Do ya see that wan over there? The turkey? Couldn't tell her anythin'. Gossip, gossip, gossip, all day and –"

Áine turned to Fionn.

"It's her ring. No doubt."

Fionn put his thumb in his mouth, pressed his thumb to the ring, and looked into the shiny stone. In the stone, both agents could clearly see the Queen talking to a tin-whistle player in Eyre Square.

"Is there a mirror anywhere?" Fionn called out to the crowd.

No-one paid him any heed. No-one, that is, bar the very smallest of the choristers.

"In the church," he said. "Follow me!"

Áine and Fionn followed him through the heavy oak doors, to a mirror in the choir's dressing room. With a wave goodbye, they jumped through, leaving a very wide-eyed choirboy in their wake.

In Eyre Square the tin-whistle player was very helpful.

"I thought she was a busker," he said, "but she kept going on about a bull she wanted to buy. You can't buy a bull here, I told her." He shook his head. "She got a bit thick then, so I sent her out to Maam Cross – to the fair."

"Let's go!" Áine said.

The two agents looked around desperately. There was nothing. No mirror. No shiny surface anywhere to be seen.

"That shopping centre!" Áine said. "There has to be a mirror there!"

Sure enough, there was a full-size mirror in a small boutique inside the door.

The mirror road led them to a pub at Maam Cross. They rushed outside and found themselves at the fair.

The air was full of voices speaking both Irish and English – shouting, laughing and haggling.

"I'll give you five hundred!"

"Do I look like a fool?"

"Where are we?" Áine muttered.

"Connemara!" Fionn said triumphantly.
"Look over there! Those mountains are called
the Twelve Pins and –"

"Look!" Áine said. "It's Maebh!"

The two agents pushed their way through the crowds of horse dealers, hawkers and cloth-capped farmers until they stopped right beside Maebh's chariot.

The Queen was having a heated argument with a local farmer.

"I'll give you two sacks of gold for him!" Maebh was saying.

"You won't!" said the farmer. "I want five thousand euro. And not a penny less. He's a prize bull and well you know it, missus!"

Before Áine could say a word Maebh pulled her sword. The farmer raised his walking stick. Fionn grabbed the farmer's arm. "You don't want to mess with her," he said. "She was here before, and caused an almighty row over another bull."

"Maebh!" Áine shouted up at the woman in the chariot.

"Queen Maebh," she answered belligerently.

"All right! Queen Maebh. You know you're not supposed to leave the Otherworld."

"I'll go where I like," said the Queen haughtily.

The stoat growled at Áine.

"And there's no need for that kind of language either," Áine said to him, grabbing the horse's harness.

"Now listen," Fionn said to the farmer, "two bags of gold is worth a lot more than 5000 euros. Let her have the bull."

The farmer frowned. "Let me see the gold!"

Maebh threw two bags on to the ground. "There!" she shouted.

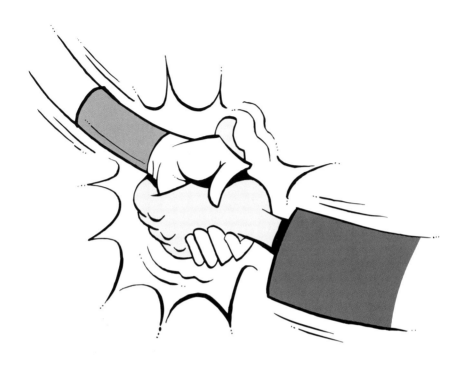

The farmer bent down and examined the loot. Then he stood up.

He spat on his hand and offered it to Maebh. To Fionn and Áine's amazement, the Queen spat on her own hand, and shook the farmer's hand with great force.

"*Bíodh sé ina mhargadh!*" she said. "It's a deal."

Fionn turned to Áine and grinned.

Just then there was a mighty peal of thunder. The image of Maebh, the chariot and the bull all started to shimmer in the rapidly fading light. There was one more ferocious roar from the sky, followed by a flash of pure blue lightning, and Maebh, chariot and bull disappeared.

"Phew!" said Áine. "That's her settled." She turned to the farmer. "Thank you for giving her the bull," she said to him with a radiant smile.

"No problem," the old man said. "I was glad to be shut of him!"

Fionn and Áine looked at one another and burst out laughing.

"We'd better be off," Fionn said, when they sobered up.

Áine looked around wistfully. "Pity we can't stay a while . . ."

"I know," Fionn said, "but with our luck there's probably already someone else out there looking to start trouble!"

"Let's hope there are no bulls involved this time!" Áine said, as she and Fionn made for the nearest mirror and home.

GALWAY

WESTSIDE PLAYING FIELDS

University College Hospital

National University of Ireland

Galway Cathedral

Galway Hibernians Soccer Club

Galway Sportsground

St. Nicholas Church

Druid Lane

Spanish Arch

Galway Business Enterprise Park

Eyre Square

Galway City Museum

River Corrib

Lough Atalia

THE DOCKS

THE CLADDAGH

NEWCASTLE

SHANTALA

FR. BURKE PARK

SOUTH PARK

SALTHILL

MERVUE UNITED A.F.C.

RENMORE

BOHERMORE CEMETERY

CLARENBRIDGE

NEW DOCKS

Ten Fun Facts About Galway!

1. The longest place name in Ireland is Muckanaghederdauhaulia in County Galway. It means "piggery between two salt-water places" in Irish.

2. Grace O'Malley, the famous pirate from Connaught, was called *Gráinne Mhaol* (Bald Gráinne) because she cut off all her hair when her father told her she couldn't work on his ships because her hair would get caught in the ropes.

3. A Claddagh ring has two hands holding a crowned heart on it. If worn on the right hand with the tip of the heart pointing to the fingers, the wearer is looking for love. If on the left hand with the heart pointing to the wrist, the wearer is married.

4. If the Claddagh fishermen met a woman with red hair, or anything red-haired, they believed that was bad luck and they would not go fishing. Butchers used to release a fox near the boats – if there was no fish, people bought meat!

5. In 1990 the statue of the famous writer Pádraic Ó Conaire in Eyre Square was beheaded by vandals. Happily, the head was retrieved and since then Pádraic has lived in the safety of Galway Museum.

6. Christopher Columbus prayed in the Church of St Nicholas on his way to discover America. St Nicholas is the patron saint of seafarers and children (he is the original Santa Claus).

7. Humanity Dick Martin from Galway was called 'Humanity' because of his campaigns against cruelty to animals. He once had a donkey appear in court as a witness against his abuser!

8. James Lynch Fitzstephen, Mayor of Galway, in 1493 hanged his own son from the balcony of his house after convicting him of murdering a Spanish tourist. It's thought that this is where the expression "lynching" comes from.

9. Galway man Adrian Walsh is a ball control hero. He made the Guinness Book of Records in 1978, 1979 and finally in 1980 when he managed "keepie-uppies" for over 4 hours.

10. On 15th August 1970 a hurricane blew up on Inis Mór, the largest of the Aran Islands. Locals had to sit in the plane that serviced the three islands to prevent it from being blown away!

If you enjoyed this book from
Poolbeg why not visit our website:

www.poolbeg.com

and get another book delivered straight
to your home or to a friend's home.

All books despatched within 24 hours.

POOLBEG

Why not join our mailing list
at www.poolbeg.com and get some
fantastic offers, competitions,
author interviews and much more?

@PoolbegBooks